Psst!...Look Up! Can you reach for the stars?

For Loo, Owen and Elliot

First published in 2017 by Baker-Duly Books

10 9 8 7 6 5 4 3 2 1

Written by Caroline Trowbridge Illustrated by Lehla Eldridge

Designed by Lehla Eldridge and Caroline Trowbridge carolinetrowbridge.com lehlaeldridge.com

ISBN 260743156569304

Thank you to NASA for their images used in this book.

"to die will be an awfully big adventure!" Peter Pan, by J.M Barrie

Written by Caroline Trowbridge

Illustrated by Lehla Eldridge

That’s all folks!
I’m blasting out of here!

I'm off then, kid. So long now!
Keep smiling through the tears.

Tummy tickles, body tingles,
soaring through the sky.
Look at me! I'm Peter Pan!
I finally can fly!

Did you see me shoot?
I'm higher than the moon!
I'm speeding to the Milky Way,
planet Earth, I'll see you soon!

I'm darting past you Venus,
seeking Mercury and Mars…

Watch out, planet Jupiter!
I'm headed for the stars!

A trillion miles an hour-
there's no stopping me up here!
I'm racing, chasing, spinning rings
around Saturn's atmosphere!

So long, Uranus and Neptune!
This is awesome! Wow!
I'm smashing through the asteroid belt-
nothing can stop me now!

See, I am made of star dust,
so, it's like home up here!
A giant ball of energy
shoots me to the stratosphere!

Remember, we are made of stars.
It's how all life began.
The Universe is inside us, kid-
starting out from one Big Bang!

So, watch me from your window,
when you're lonely or full of dread…

…then make a wish upon me
and I'll guide you back to bed.

Don’t be sad!
Just think of me shining
bright and full of power!

I'm shooting down,
with old friends around,
in a space-tacular meteor shower!

Well, time is a ticking,
so, try not to forget,
to give thanks for all the memories
and celebrate that we met.

We’re connected, You and I, kid,
in this Universal family.
I can see it clear as stars now:
Love is our destiny.

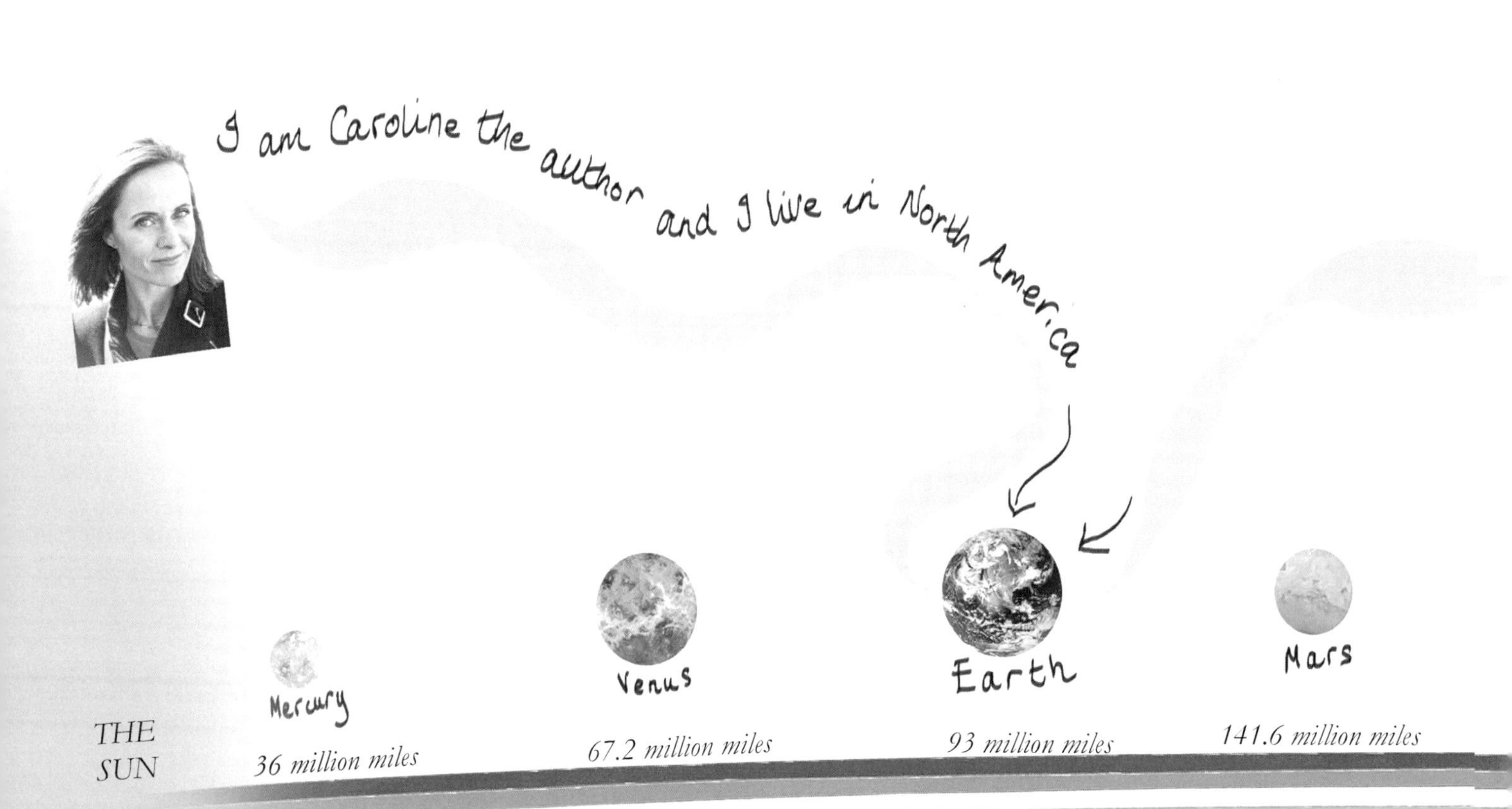

Caroline and Lehla last worked together on the children's picture book I am Me…You, Us and We (Baker-Duly Books) but originally met as young actors at The Guildhall School of Music and Drama, London. Born in England, Caroline worked for over 20 years as an actor in television, film and theatre, which is where she met her husband, Edward. They have two children, Miles and Iris and live in New York where she still loves to act, give Reiki (she is a Reiki Master) and create and write books inspired by friendship, family, and humanity.

'Eternal love and gratitude to Edward, Miles and Iris.
To our dearest cat, Twiglet; We will forever look for you amidst the stars…x'

carolinetrowbridge.com

Lehla Eldridge is a writer, blogger, illustrator and sometimes performer. She has illustrated and written 'The Lovely Book for Wonderful Women' 'The South African Illustrated Cookbook' and she co-authored and illustrated 'Jump, Fall, Fly – from schooling to homeschooling to unschooling'. She has written for The Guardian and has illustrated other children's books. She loves working with Caroline as they go off into another world and create magic... She drew these pictures lovingly for all the friends and cats that flew off whilst making this book. Especially for Miss Ella Day and Zed. A big thank you to her children and husband 'I love you all beyond words'.

jumpfallfly.com lehlaeldridge.com

So, shine bright…

Lightning Source UK Ltd.
Milton Keynes UK
UKRC02n2202131117
312683UK00001B/4